I'LL FLIP YOU FOR IT, BEETLE BAILEY

by Mort Walker

tempo books

GROSSET & DUNLAP
A FILMWAYS COMPANY
Publishers • New York

I'LL FLIP YOU FOR IT, BEETLE BAILEY

I HEAR THAT SO MANY GUYS WANT TO JOIN THE ARMY LATELY, WE CAN BE VERY CHOOSY

THAT'S RIGHT

11-5

CALL THE BASKETBALL COACH AND TELL HIM HIS ORDER IS IN

MORT WALKER

21! GAME AND MATCH TO SNORKEL!

I **WON!** I WON THE TOURNAMENT.!!

GET GOING, BEETLE! THE LOSER HAS TO INFORM THE PAPER!

I KNOW, I KNOW

11-6

MORT WALKER

SPORTS

BAILEY LOSES

FOUR O'CLOCK AND ALL MY WORK DONE... TOO EARLY TO GO TO THE OFFICERS' CLUB

MUCH TOO EARLY TO GO HOME

11-14

IN MY YOUTH THIS WOULD HAVE BEEN THE TIME FOR TENNIS OR HANDBALL--- AH, WELL

MORT WALKER

SOMEBODY'S GOT HIS WORK ALL DONE AGAIN

11-29

MORT WALKER

12-2

12-15

A BEAUTIFUL DIVING CATCH, BEETLE!

TOO BAD YOU SLID INTO LT. FUZZ'S FLOWER BED, THOUGH

MORI WALKER

12-17

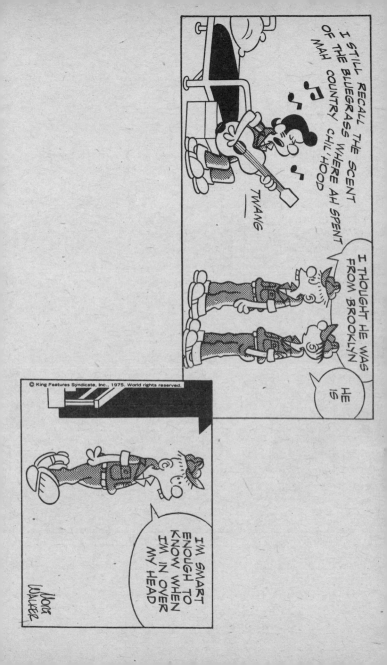

LOOK! I MADE SOME DOUGHNUT BALLS!

OPEN YOUR MOUTH AND I'LL THROW YOU ONE

12-23

CAN SOMEONE GO SIMPLE MINDED ALL AT ONCE?

MORT WALKER

1-6

I INSTALLED AN OLD EJECTOR SEAT FROM A FIGHTER PLANE IN MY JEEP

PRETTY FANCY

2-17

BUT AREN'T YOU AFRAID SOMEONE WILL SIT IN IT AND PULL THE EJECTOR LEVER?

WHAT IDIOT WOULD DO THAT?

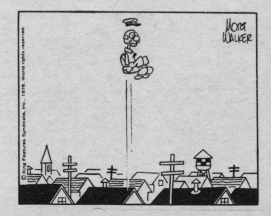

MORT WALKER

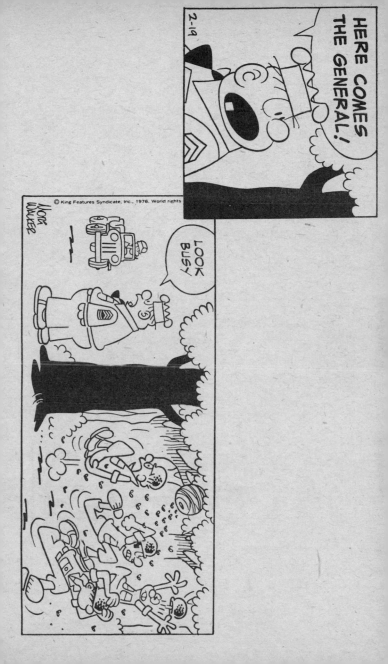

2-21

SARGE FELL OFF A CLIFF AND IS LYING UNCONSCIOUS ON A LEDGE 50 FEET DOWN!

GOSH!

2-26

GET SOME ROPE, A STRETCHER, AND A COMIC BOOK!

WHAT'S THE COMIC BOOK FOR?

WHILE YOU GUYS ARE GETTING HIM UP, I GOTTA HAVE **SOMETHING** TO DO

MORT WALKER

3-16

GENERAL, THIS IS LT. FUZZ RETURNING YOUR CALL

MY CALL? I DIDN'T CALL YOU

3-18

WHY WOULD I CALL **YOU**?

SOMEONE SAID IT WAS ABOUT MY PROMOTION

MORT WALKER

YOU'D BETTER CHECK ON THAT

I'M CHECKING NOW, SIR.

HUMMM...

3-8

BEETLE! DON'T YOU KNOW WHAT TO DO WITH THIS RAKE?

SMAK!

MORT WALKER

WHY DO YOU DO THAT?!

JUST BECAUSE IT'S THERE

OTTO

© King Features Syndicate, Inc., 1976.

Mort WALKER